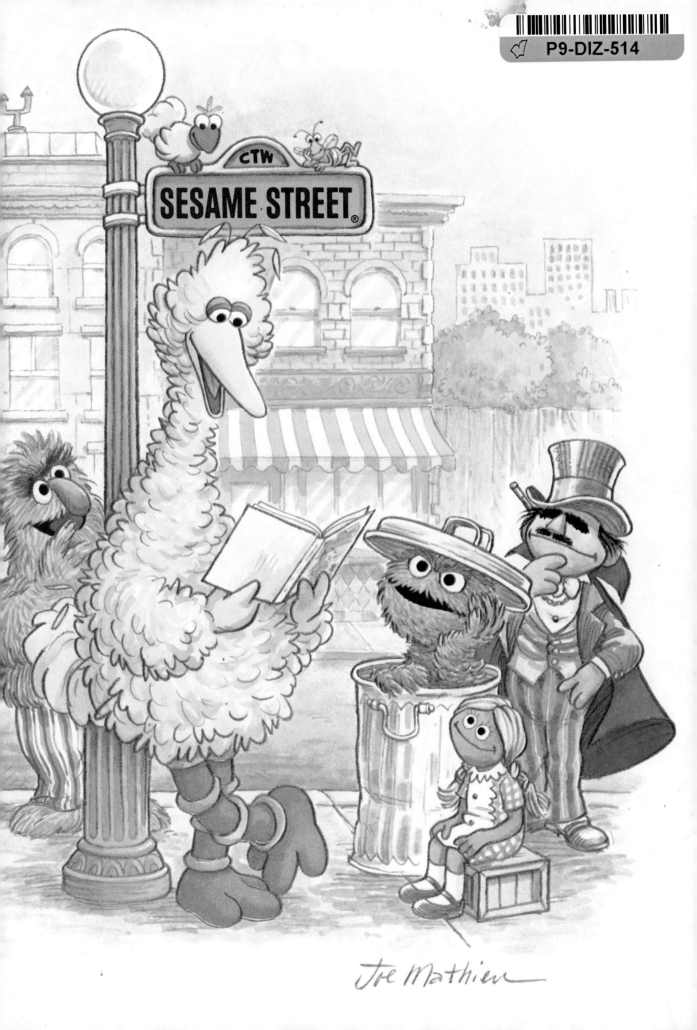

CTW

SESAME STREET®

Joe Mathieu

THE SESAME STREET® LIBRARY

With Jim Henson's Muppets

VOLUME 2

FEATURING THE LETTERS C AND D AND THE NUMBER 2

Children's Television Workshop/Funk & Wagnalls, Inc.

WRITTEN BY:
Michael Frith
Jerry Juhl
Emily Perl Kingsley
Sharon Lerner
Nina B. Link
Albert G. Miller
Jeffrey Moss
Norman Stiles
Jon Stone
Daniel Wilcox

ILLUSTRATED BY:
Mel Crawford
Peter Cross
A. Delaney
Michael Frith
Joseph Mathieu
Harry McNaught
Kelly Oechsli
Michael J. Smollin
Bob Taylor

PHOTOGRAPHS BY:
Charles P. Rowan

 Published in the United States by Random House, Inc., New York, and simultaneously in Canada by Random House of Canada Limited, Toronto, in conjunction with the Children's Television Workshop. Distributed by Funk & Wagnalls, Inc., New York, N.Y. Manufactured in the United States of America.
0-8343-0010-9
4 5 6 7 8 9 0

cC

A Poem by Cookie Monster

C is for COOKIES.
Me like them a bunch.
Me crunch them for dinner
And breakfast and lunch.

And then there are CRUMBS.
Cookie crumbs are so yummy!
Me sweep them off table
And into my tummy.

Did you know
    the word CARTON
    begins with a C?
That's the box
    cookies come in.
It tastes good to me!

Well, that's all the C words
Me got for today.
Me get in my car now
And me drive away.

Hey, wait!

The word CAR starts with C
Boy, that's neat!
Me thought me had run out of
C things to eat.

CRUNCH!

CRUNCH!

CRUNCH!

Tasty —
But not as good as
COOKIE!

Bye-bye!

The Perils of Penelope

Then Penelope went outside.

Unfortunately, Penelope had walked between two charging rhinoceroses.

Fortunately, a Young-Hero-Crane-Operator came along and used his crane to lift Penelope up to higher ground.

Fear not, Penelope! I, the Young-Hero-Crane-Operator, will use my crane to lift you up to higher ground!

Thank goodness!

I Used to Be Afraid

by Grover and Ernie

When I was little I used to be scared
Of being alone in the night.
I'd pull the blankets up over my head
And pray that the sky would get light...

But then my mommy sat by my bed
And said there was nothing to fear,
'Cause nothing scary went on in the night
And she and my daddy were near.

When I was little I used to be scared
Of taking a bath in the tub.
I thought when the water ran down the drain
That I would go with it...Glub-Glub.

But my old buddy Bert said,
"Come on, use your brain.
If you just take a look, you will see
That you NEVER could fit
through that very small drain!"

Now my tubby's where I love to be.

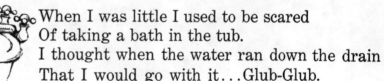

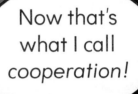

Sleeping Beauty

Just because she wasn't invited to a party, a bad fairy once cast a spell on a little baby princess.

"When she is sixteen, the princess will prick her finger on a needle and die," she screeched.

Luckily there were some good fairies around. One of them quickly said, "The princess won't die. She will only sleep for a hundred years until a handsome prince comes to wake her up."

Sure enough, though she had been taught to be very careful, the princess did prick her finger while spinning yarn in the tower on her sixteenth birthday. She fell asleep at once.

And so did everyone else in the castle. All the maids and footmen, the king and the queen, the horses and dogs and cats. Everyone.

So many trees and weeds and thorny bushes grew up around the sleeping castle that it became almost impossible to find.

After a hundred years had gone by, a handsome prince cut his way through the bushes. He found the sleeping princess. She was so beautiful that he kissed her gently on the cheek. She woke up.

Everyone woke up—the maids and the footmen, the king and the queen, the horses and dogs and cats.

Soon afterward the prince and princess were married, and they lived happily ever after.

Cookie Monster's Butterfly Cookies

COOKIES GRATIA COOKIES

What? You hungry again? Well... YOU IN LUCK! It time to make
BUTTERFLY COOKIES.

First, get out your dough. What? You need more?
O.K. Look at Volume 1 for cookie dough recipe.

Ready now? We going to make some COOKIE PAINT!

1. First get some evaporated milk
   (or mix 1 egg yolk with ¼ teaspoon of water).
   Then get some cups and put a little milk or
   egg mixture in each one.

2. Now add some food coloring to each cup. You get
   COOKIE PAINT! If paint gets too thick, just
   add a few drops of water.

Now sprinkle cloth with flour and roll
out dough on it, about ¼ inch thick.

Cut little strip of dough for middle of
butterfly.

Next come wings—You remember how to
make circle cookies? Just press down glass
and peel away extra dough.

Then cut circle in half ...

Now put pieces together like this ...

And PAINT with your pretty cookie
paint ... and you have a BEAUTIFUL
butterfly.

Now heat oven to 400
degrees. Put butter-
flies on ungreased
cookie sheet and
COOK 6 to 8 minutes.

REMEMBER! Never use oven
without grown-up helping you.

Now what we do
while butterflies
cook?
ME KNOW!

We can play game on
next page.

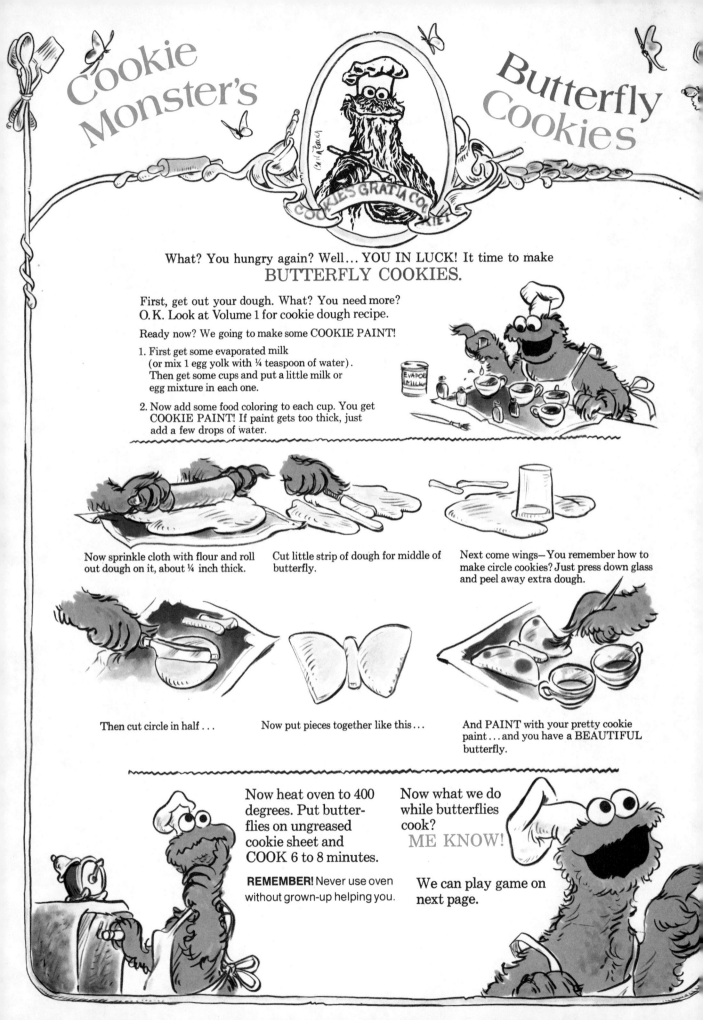

Do you know where all the GOOD THINGS that go into Cookie Monster's FAMOUS COOKIE DOUGH come from? Well, you gonna find out now! Just follow the paths.

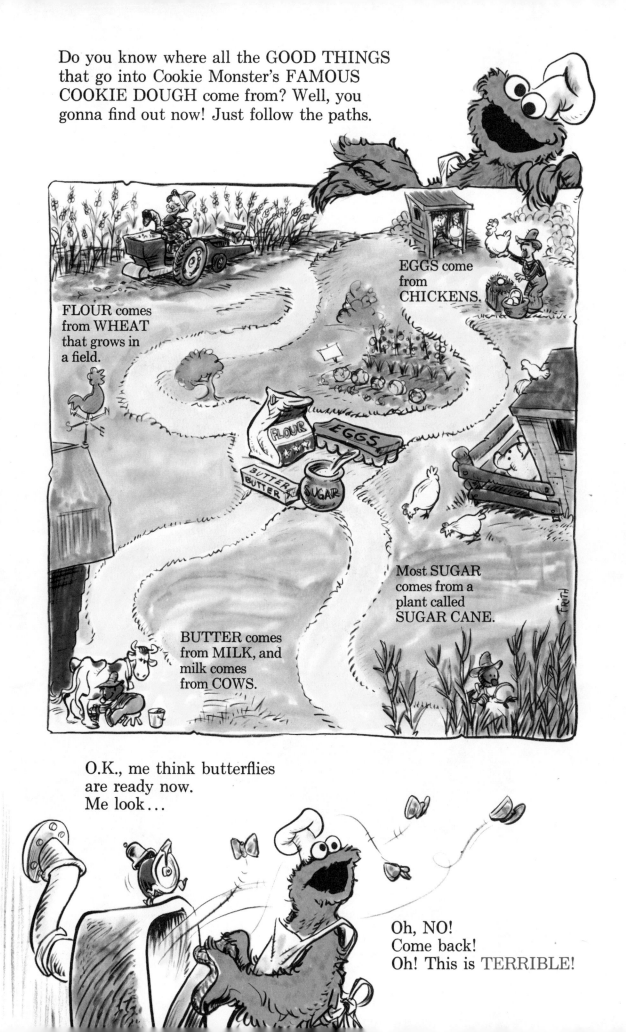

FLOUR comes from WHEAT that grows in a field.

EGGS come from CHICKENS.

Most SUGAR comes from a plant called SUGAR CANE.

BUTTER comes from MILK, and milk comes from COWS.

O.K., me think butterflies are ready now. Me look...

Oh, NO! Come back! Oh! This is TERRIBLE!

Grover and Betty Lou, Plumbers

In this story there are dozens of words that begin with the letter D. So listen carefully and see how many D-words you can count. This story is called

THE DIAMOND D
AND THE DREADFUL DRAGON

ozens of years ago, in a drafty castle, Duke David of Dundeedle did dwell. Duke David was dumpy, but dignified. And he had a darling daughter named Dora who was a delight.

One day Dora danced through the door in a dear little dress decorated with daffodils. "Doodley-doo, doodley-doo," Dora sang, as she danced. "Oh, hello, dear, dumpy daddy," said Dora to Duke David of Dundeedle.

"Dora, my darling, dimpled daughter," said Duke David. "You are indeed delightful, so I have a dandy present for you."

"Do tell," said Dora. "Do describe this doo-dad, daddy."

"It is a dazzling diamond D dangling from a chain!" So, hanging the D around Dora's dimpled neck, Duke David of Dundeedle departed through the door.

Dora also departed, darting down into the daisy patch to dance amid the Duke's downy ducks.

Although Dora and Duke David didn't know it, someone else dwelt in the castle. This someone was Donald, the Dreadful Dragon of Dundeedle.

"I am Donald, the Dreadful Dragon of Dundeedle. I live in a dungeon downstairs in Duke David's dwelling. It is a deep dungeon, a dark dungeon—a deep, dark, damp, dank, dreary dungeon. It is a dump!"

Donald used dozens of D words—which was the only nice thing you could say about him. Otherwise he was a dud.

Donald the Dragon dashed from his dungeon, directly to Duke David's dandy daisy patch. "I am dashing from my dungeon to steal the diamond D that Duke David gave his daughter Dora," he said.

Donald, the doer of dark deeds, drifted into the daisy patch. Dora, daughter of Duke David, saw the dreadful dragon and dropped a drooping daisy from her dainty dimpled hand. She danced directly up to Donald the Dragon and declared, "Well, look who's here—a dear doggie! Hi there, doggie."

Donald disbelieved his droopy ears. "*Doggie?*" he screamed. "Did you say *doggie?*"

"Definitely," said Dora.

"Well, I do declare!" said Donald. "If Dora, the dignified Duke David's daughter, thinks that I, Donald the Dreadful Dragon of Dundeedle, am a doggie, then Dora is *dumb!*"

"But you're the dearest doggie I've ever seen," Dora declared. "Do come and dwell in our castle, doggie dear, and I'll give you this Diamond D which my doting daddy draped around my dimpled neck."

"Don't 'doggie' me!" Donald roared, darting toward Dora, determined to grab the Diamond D.

Suddenly, Duke David dashed into the daisy patch. Diving between darling Dora and Dreadful Donald, the Duke drove Donald around and around the daisy patch. The dismal dragon ducked, dodged, darted and dashed through the ducklings and the daisies until the Duke dumped him into the duck pond.

"Daddy dear," said Dora, "why did you do that?"

"Because that dreadful, dishonest dragon was determined to steal the dazzling Diamond D from around your dainty, dimpled neck," said the Duke.

"Dragon?" said Dora. "I'll be darned! He looked like a doggie to *me*."

"You're dumb but you're adorable, Dora," said Duke David, "so here's what we'll do. From this day on this dreadful dragon will dwell in a dog house, dine on dog biscuits, and do doggie tricks to delight my divine daughter Dora—*or else!*"

"Or else what?" Donald demanded.

"I'll dump you in the duck pond again!"

"Bow-wow," said Donald. "I'm a doggie."

And so David, Duke of Dundeedle, and his delightful daughter Dora lived happily ever after with Donald the Doggie who used to be a dreadful dragon.

Grover's Neighborhood Games

Hello, everybodeeee!

I, Grover have a wonderful new GUESSING GAME.

You pretend you are a person who works in your neighborhood and act out your job. See if your friends can guess who you are.

When I play, I pretend to put out a big fire with a hose.

Can you guess who I am?

Did you say a *fireman?*

Ooooh! You are SO SMART!

Sometimes I like to dress up like different people in the neighborhood Here are some of my FAVORITE costumes.

GROVER THE MAILMAN—Make a mail bag for your letters out of a paper folder. Use cardboard or construction paper to make a hat.

GROVER THE POLICEMAN—Cover a round piece of cardboard with silver foil for a badge. Make a police hat out of cardboard.

All right, now—open wide. Say "Aaaahhh . . ." Oh, what cute tonsils you have!

GROVER THE DOCTOR—Hang a spool of thread around your neck on a string for a stethoscope. An old shoe box can be your doctor's bag. Fill it with empty bottles and bandages made out of some clean rags.

Roosevelt Franklin Washes His Dog

Here is Roosevelt Franklin filling the tub with water.

Roosevelt is taking his dog, Night Train, over to the tub.

Roosevelt is putting Night Train into the tub.

Roosevelt is giving Night Train a nice scrub.

There. See how clean Night Train is! And Roosevelt did it ALL BY HIMSELF. Good for you, Roosevelt Franklin!

2

Sherlock Hemlock
in
"The Mysterious Stranger"

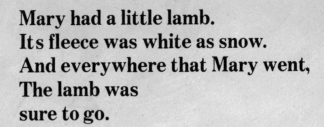

Mary had a little lamb.
Its fleece was white as snow.
And everywhere that Mary went,
The lamb was
sure to go.

The Case of the Missing Letter

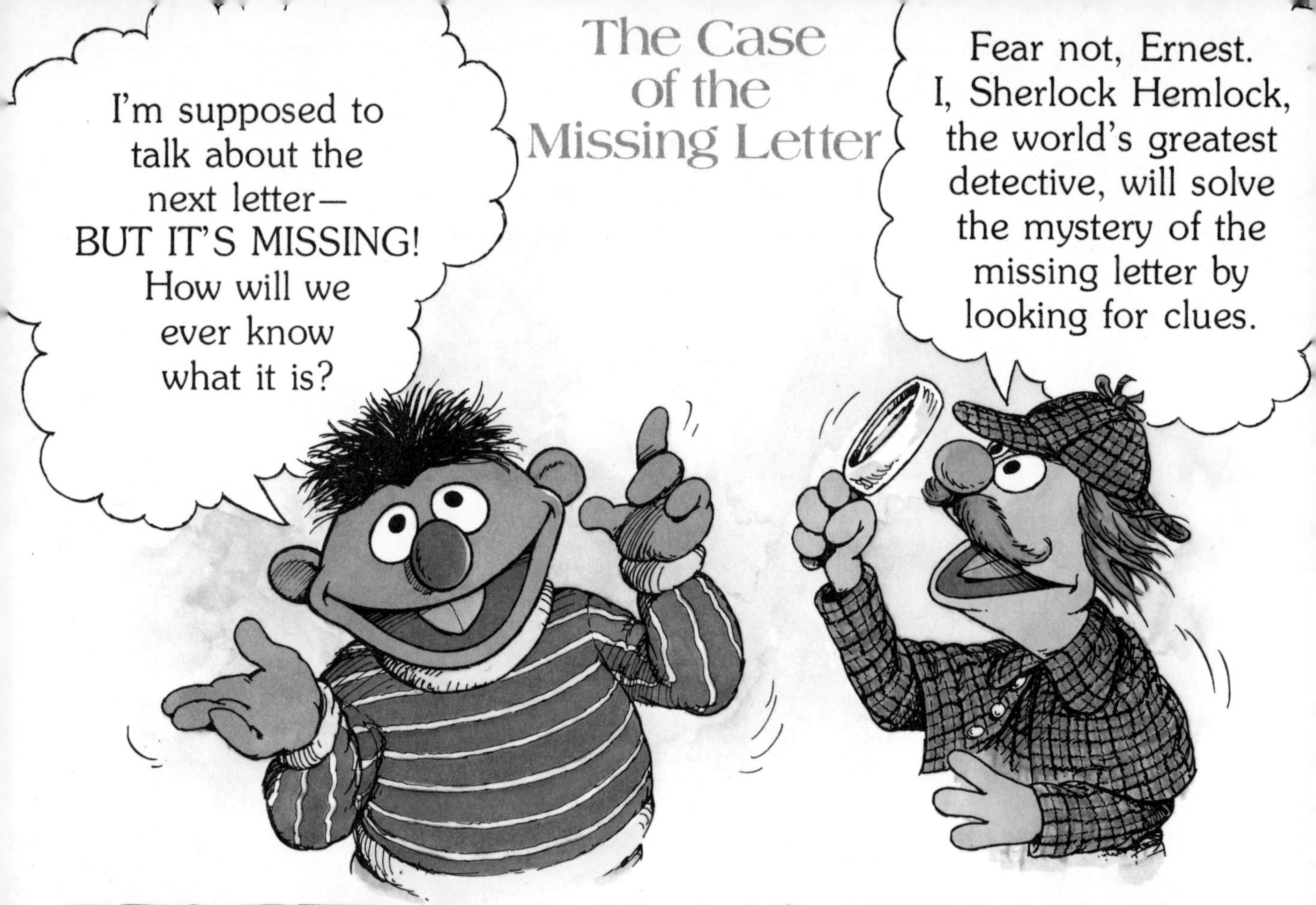

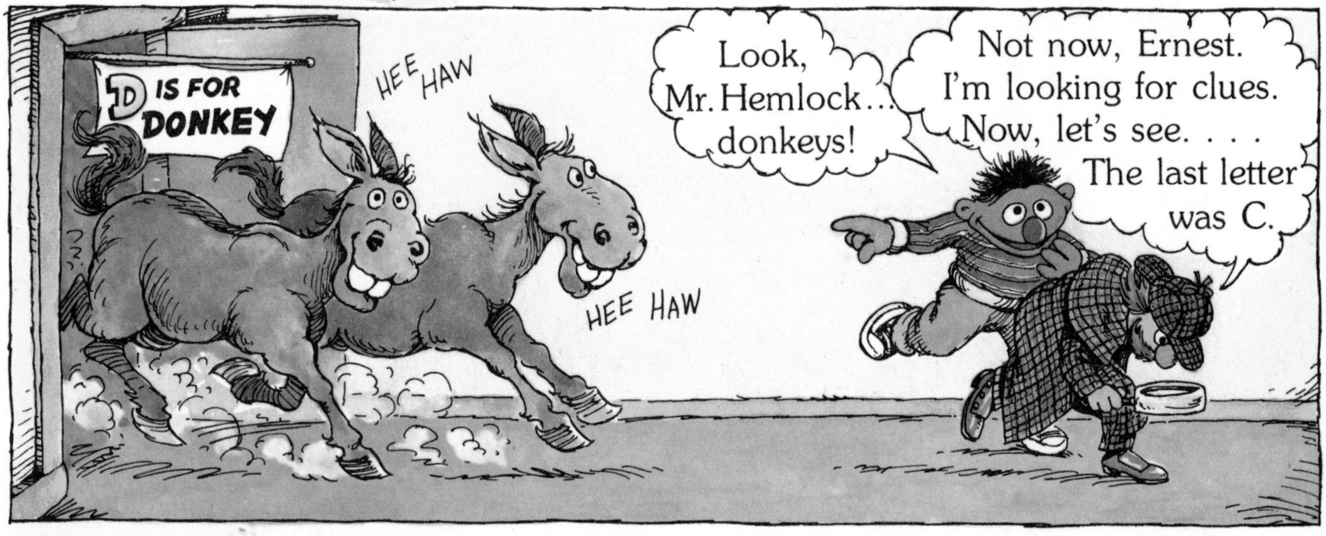

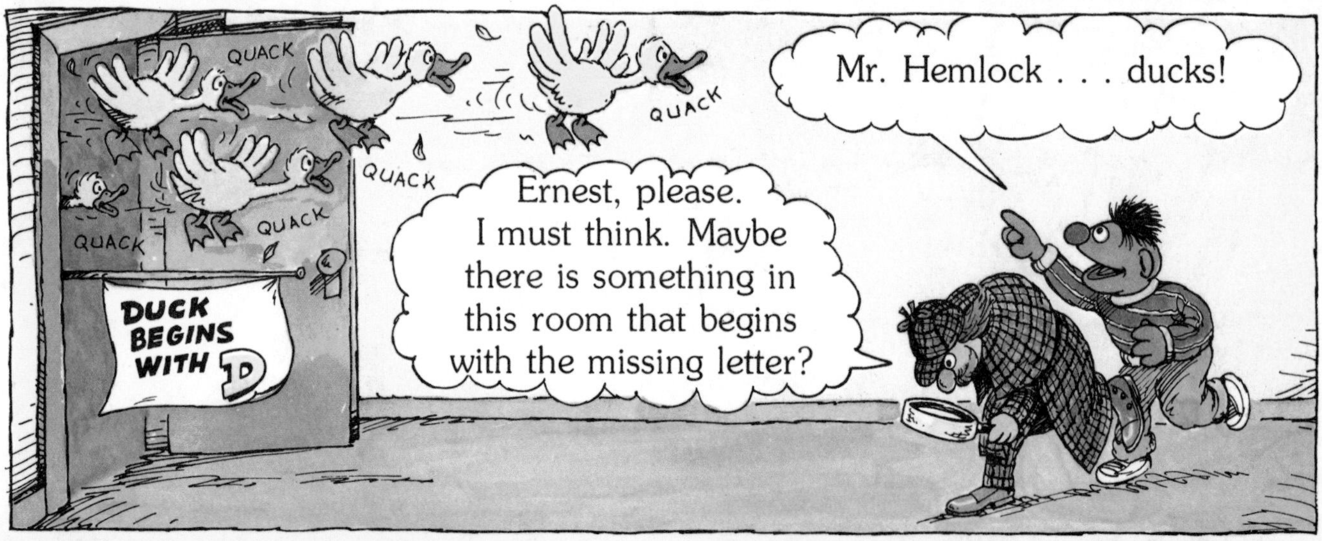